CASEFILE:
ARKHAM

"NIGHTMARE ON CANVAS"

CREATED BY

JOSH FINNEY   &   PATRICK McEVOY

CASEFILE: ARKHAM
"NIGHTMARE ON CANVAS"

WRITTEN BY
JOSH FINNEY

ART BY
PATRICK McEVOY

EDITOR
KAT ROCHA

Hank Flynn created by Josh Finney & Patrick McEvoy

Published by 01Publishing.

ISBN 10: 098392306X

ISBN 13: 978-0-9839230-6-0

Printed in China

www.01Publishing.com
"No Safe Space."

PROLOGUE

MURDER! ON NEWBURY STREET

SPLASH!

HELP!

SOMEONE PLEASE!

DON'T LOOK BACK, DELIA!

JUST KEEP RUNNING!

RRRAAAH!!

CHAPTER ONE

"Hell is a state of mind."

"...THE BOSTON ART CLUB."

ARKHAM
MUSEUM
OF
LIVING ARTISTS

DERLITH HAD OFFERED UP A WHOLE BUCKET OF CRAZY AS TO WHY PICKMAN MAY'VE GONE MISSING.

BLACKMAIL...

AMNESIA...

KIDNAPPED BY JEALOUS RIVALS.

BUT A GILDED CAGE WILL ONLY HOLD AN ANIMAL LIKE PICKMAN FOR SO LONG...

...EVEN WHEN IT COMES WRAPPED IN A SILK DRESS AND HAS ACCESS TO A DEAD HUSBAND'S FORTUNE.

PICKMAN WAS LONG GONE.

THAT MUCH I WAS SURE OF.

MAYBE HE WAS JUST LAYING LOW, OR VANISHED TO THE NEXT TOWN OVER.

WHEREVER HE'D GOTTEN TO, I WAS SURE OF ONE THING...

HE'D LEFT FOR GREENER, YOUNGER FIELDS TO PLOW.

CHAPTER TWO

"Sharing the world with slaughtered pigs."

YESTERDAY, EVERYTHING ABOUT THIS
CASE TOLD ME IT WAS A DUD. A DAY
OR TWO'S WORK FOR A QUICK
HUNDRED BUCKS. BUT NOW...

...I FELT AS THOUGH SOMEONE WAS
TRYING TO SQUEEZE ME INTO THE
PUNCH LINE OF AN ELABORATE JOKE.

QUESTION WAS, WHO WOULD
I FIND LAUGHING AT THE END?
DERLITH? PICKMAN? OR WOULD
IT BE THIS CRAZY SWAMI I WAS
ABOUT TO MEET?

MADAM BALTHAZAR.

HER REAL NAME WAS **MARTHA
PRICHARD**, AND FROM WHAT I
COULD TELL, THE LADY HAD BEEN
IN THE FAKE-A-LOO BUSINESS
FOR A LONG, LONG TIME.

AMAZING WHAT YOU CAN DIG UP
ON A PERSON JUST BY THUMBING
THROUGH OLD PHONE BOOKS.

BEING THE GOOD CATHOLIC BOY
I AM, I KNEW THE ROUTINE.

CRYING STATUES...

VIRGIN APPARITIONS...

BE IT A BIBLE OR A CRYSTAL
BALL, IT WAS ALL THE SAME
GAME. PARTING RUBES FROM
THEIR HARD EARNED CASH.

THESE DAYS...

...MY FAITH DIDN'T COME SO CHEAP.

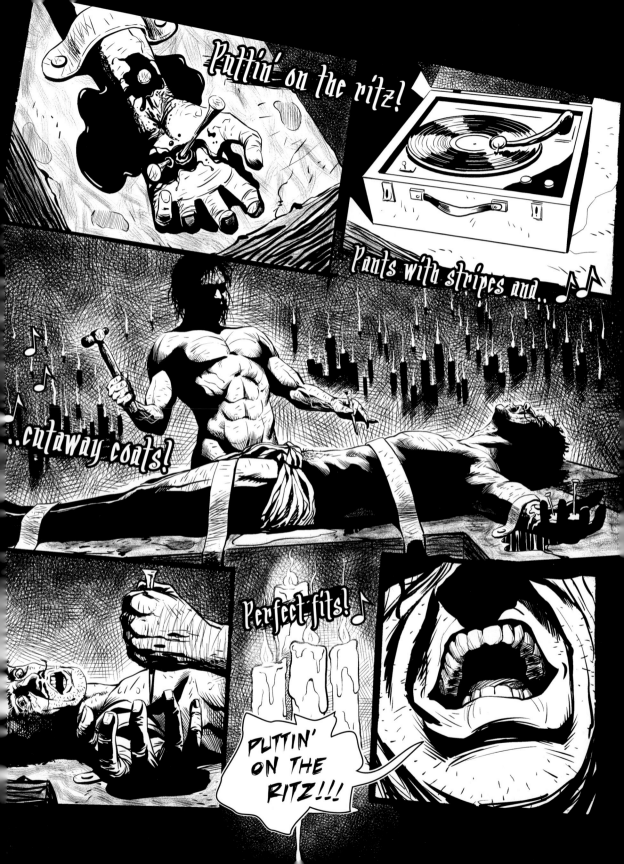

CHAPTER THREE

"Sometimes there are no good answers."

ON THE EDGE OF THE CITY WHERE THE RIVER SMELLS OF OIL AND ROT AND THE HIGHWAY LEANS TOWARD DUNWICH...

...THERE'S A PATCH OF UGLY CALLED DREDGER'S END.

IN THE OLD DAYS THIS HAD ALL BEEN MUD.

A DOT ON THE MAP BORN OUT OF HALF A CENTURY OF DREDGING CREWS DUMPING THEIR WASTE.

NOW IT'S A PLACE WHERE CRIME HIDES IN PLAN SIGHT.

WHERE GRIFTERS THRIVE, SIN IS CHEAP, AND THE DESPERATE AND DOWNTRODDEN COME TO GRAB HOLD OF WHATEVER COMFORT THEY CAN AFFORD.

BE IT A STIFF DRINK...

A WARM BODY...

OR A PUFF OF THE MID-NIGHT OIL.

ME? I WAS THERE ON BUSINESS.

PICKMAN'S FORTE WAS FACES.

I DON'T BELIEVE ANYBODY SINCE GOYA COULD PUT SO MUCH SHEER HELL INTO A SET OF FEATURES.

IT HADN'T BEEN HARD TO GET THURBER TALKING...OR DRINKING. BEFORE I'D EVEN ARRIVED HE'D STARTED IN ON A BOTTLE OF EIGHTY PROOF TRUTH SERUM.

THEN AGAIN, ONE MAN'S TRUTH CAN OFTEN AMOUNT TO AN EAR FULL OF NOTHING IF THE GUY'S ALREADY A BIT SOFT IN THE HEAD.

THOSE ACCURSED FACES LEERED AND SLAVERED OUT OF THE CANVAS WITH THE VERY BREATH OF LIFE!

BY GOD, MAN!

I VERILY BELIEVE THEY WERE ALIVE!

THAT NAUSEOUS WIZARD, PICKMAN, HAD WAKED THE FIRES OF HELL IN PIGMENT! AS IF HIS BRUSH HAD BEEN A NIGHTMARE-SPAWNING WAND!

COLD BEEF

LET'S HAVE A SMALL DOSE OF STRAIGHT TALK, HERE.

YOU SAY YOU WERE THE LAST TO SEE PICKMAN.

BUT YOU WON'T GO TO THE COPS.

"THAT ALONE MAKES YOU A SUSPECT."

EXCUSE ME?!

SUSPECTED OF WHAT?!

YOU COULDN'T POSSIBLY BELIEVE ME CAPABLE OF...I MEAN, WHY WOULD I BE HELPING YOU IF I WERE GUILTY OF...OF...

ANYTHING ILLEGAL OR UNTOWARD?

A LOTTA THINGS.

NONE OF THEM GOOD.

HEY, I'M JUST SAYING HOW IT LOOKS FROM MY SIDE OF THE TABLE. FOR THE RECORD, NO...

...I DON'T THINK YA DID ANYTHING WRONG...NOTHING PRISON-WORTHY AT LEAST.

I AWOKE TO THE SOUND OF VOICES.

VERY LOUD, VERY STUPID VOICES.

OH BOO-FUCKIN'-HOO!

I JUST SPENT THE LAST HALF *FUCKIN'* HOUR PULLIN' WHISKEY BOTTLE OUTTA MY FACE!

YOU SEE ME CRYING?

THEY TALKED LIKE A COUPLE OF HEELS.

BUT I JUST BOUGHT THIS SUIT!

IT WAS BRAND *SPANKIN'* NEW!

THE TWO OF THEM WERE OBVIOUSLY MOB.

PROBABLY HATCHETMEN.

YA KNOW, I KEEP WAITING FOR THE PART WHERE YOU EXPLAIN WHY I SHOULD CARE.

GUYS WHO ARE SO SHORT ON GRAY MATTER THEY AREN'T GOOD FOR MUCH OTHER THAN PULLING TRIGGERS AND BREAKING BONES.

DUMB, BUT DANGEROUS.

LAUREL, IT OFFENDS ME THAT YOU DON'T SYMPATHIZE WITH HOW HARD IT IS FOR ME TO SHOP FOR CLOTHES!

EVERYTHING I OWN NEEDS TO BE CUSTOM TAILORED ON ACCOUNT OF MY HAVING ABNORMALLY BROAD SHOULDERS AND A THICK NECK!

THEN AGAIN, MY OWN GREY MATTER WASN'T WORKING TOO WELL, EITHER.

CAN IT!

FOR THE LOVE OF MOTHER HYDRA, I'LL BUY YA A NEW SUIT WHEN WE GET BACK TO INNSMOUTH IF IT'LL SHUT YOU UP!

AND MY HEAD...

JESUS.

MY HEAD RANG LIKE LIKE A CHURCH BELL.

THAT AIN'T THE POINT!

IT'S THE *PRINCIPLE* OF THE MATTER. IT'S *HIM* WHAT SHOULD BE DOING THE BUYING!

I SAID ENOUGH, HARDY!

NOW MAKE LIKE AN ALARM CLOCK AND WAKE UP THIS LOUSY SHITBIRD!

CHAPTER FOUR

"Set thine house in order..."

GLYNDA HAD BEEN RIGHT ABOUT ONE THING...

WITH A FULL MEAL IN MY BELLY, THE FOG HAD LIFTED FROM MY BRAIN JUST ENOUGH FOR THE JIGSAW PIECES TO BEGIN FALLING INTO PLACE.

MINOT'S CARVED UP CORPSE... WHAT WAS IT DOING IN PICKMAN'S CELLAR? BEING TURNED INTO FINE ART, OBVIOUSLY.

BUT HOW'D IT GET THERE?

I'LL NEED TO SWING BY MY OFFICE FIRST.

TO GET MY PIECE.

AFTER LAST NIGHT, I'M NOT TAKING CHANCES.

"NOT TAKING CHANCES," HE SAYS.

HOW HAD PICKMAN MANAGED TO DRAG A GROWN MAN INTO HIS STUDIO; TORTURE HIM, KILL HIM, AND THEN VANISH AGAIN?

RIGHT UNDER THE NOSES OF THOSE TWO GOONS WHO'D BEEN CASING THE JOINT?

BUT THE HEADLINE IN THE PAPER...IT HAD GOTTEN ME THINKING.

SOMETHING THURBER HAD SAID ABOUT...

I CAN'T USE IT, NOW.

...THE SUBWAY.

I WON'T EVEN GO DOWN INTO CELLARS ANY LONGER.

THEY'RE NOT SAFE!

IF I WAS RIGHT, I FIGURED OUT WHAT HAD...

...KNOCKED HIM SCARED.

AS I RAN DOWN THAT TUNNEL...

CLICK!

...A NAGGING THOUGHT HAD CLAWED ITS WAY INTO MY MIND.

WAS THIS EVEN REAL?

OR ANOTHER NIGHTMARE?

RRRAAAH!!!

MAGIC.

HOW'D YOU KNOW TO FIND ME?

DID YOU FIND WHAT YOU WERE SEARCHING FOR?

SHOT HIM.

PUT A SLUG RIGHT INTO PICKMAN'S FACE.

GOOD.

HERE...

BROUGHT IT BACK...

...JUST LIKE I SAID WOULD.

WHY DON'T YOU HOLD ON TO IT.

I MAY WANT YOU TO...

...BRING IT BACK TO ME AGAIN, SOMETIME.

CHAPTER FIVE

"I never looked back."

I NEVER LOOKED BACK.

That evening, the Arkham PD received an "anonymous" tip, a message for one Detective Billy Sinclair.

Seems a concerned citizen decided it was his "civic duty" to hand the good detective everything he needed to close the Newbury Slasher case.

For his troubles, all Sinclair had to do was...

...LEAVE ME OUTTA THIS.

YOU FOUND HIM IN THE ACT.

YOU PUT ALL THOSE BULLETS IN HIM.

JUST LIKE THAT, HUH?

Yeah. Just like that.

Sinclair got to be hero for a day.

am's Newspaper since 1899.
lation 14,000. Available in
wich, Innsmouth, Ipswitch,
sport, Wynnaquate River,
on, and Martin's Beach.

0000781 NO. 130

MORNING
EDITION
ENTS

AF

LASHER SHOT DEAD!

gn of Terror
led By Brave
ice Officer!

KILLER , LOVER,

FIN

Arkham's uptown elite could again rest easy.

that has terrorized Arkham's Newbury
ast six months ended yesterday when
n L. Sinclair shot and killed the infa-
Slasher. The slasher, revealed to be a
named Richard Upton Pickman, had
e act of brutally murdering uptown
nor Derleth in her home. Although
save Miss Derleth from the murder-
ctive Sinclair ended monster's reign
hot Pickman six ti

Today the name Richard Upton Pickman is on everybody's lips! Yes, he was the horrible murderer known as the N Slasher, but did he was also a failed painter? It's true! Some

And me?

I walked away without stepping on any toes.

As always, there were still loose ends. Questions unanswered. Missing pieces of the puzzle.

I never did quite figure out what Martha Prichard's (a.k.a. Madam Balthazar) beef was with Pickman, or why she'd bothered conning Derleth into hiring me.

I'd waited a few days for the dust to settle, before deciding to pay the Madam another visit. She was long gone.

My guess? Sinclair's boys had probably come sniffing around, full of questions about her nephew. So she'd vanished. Skipped town.

Prichard, Balthazar, or whatever she chooses to call herself next, she'll turn up eventually.

Her type always do.

STEP RIGHT UP!

THE MYSTERIES OF THE OCCULT ARE REVEALED!

MEET THE GREAT KARLA LOMBARDI!

CHANNELER! AND MYSTIC PROGNOSTICATOR OF THE ASTRAL UNKNOWN!

DARE TO LET MADAM LOMBARDI SHOW YOU THE DARKNESS BEYOND THE BOUNDS OF INFINITY!

ONLY FIFTY CENTS!

Killing Derleth would make him famous...

That's what Pickman had told me before I shot him. It was pure bunk, the broken logic of a busted mind. But I'm coming to learn reality itself isn't entirely sane.

The crazy son of a bitch was right. Turning a local socialite into wall art was the best career move of his life.

Pickman's paintings were the hottest property to hit the scene since Vincent Van Gogh's ear. At least that's what one Innsmouth art dealer was saying. Edward Sturgeon (Big Eddy to his friends) stood to make a mint auctioning off...

...BIGGEST COLLECTION OF ORIGINAL PICKMANS THIS SIDE OF HELL!

DON'T BE A DAY LATE AND A DOLLAR SHORT!

OWN ONE OF PICKMAN'S VISIONS OF UNSPEAKABLE HORROR!

So what was it Big Eddy had on Pickman?

How'd a two-bit artist living in a dump on the North End indebt himself to a mid-level Innsmouth Mafioso with a flare for the dramatic and a poor taste in hats?

More loose ends.

More questions without answers.

Answers I would never run down.

CELEBRATE THE CULT

The Elder Gods, chaos be upon them, thank the following acolytes
for their valued sacrifice to make this tome possible.